ORPHEUS and EURIDICE

Opera in Four Acts

Music by

C. W. von Gluck

Libretto by
RANIERI DE CALZABIGI

English Translation by
WALTER DUCLOUX

Ed. 2323

G. SCHIRMER
NEW YORK

NOTE

PREFACE

For almost a century, Christoph Willibald Gluck (1714-1787) has been the earliest operatic composer represented in the repertory of opera houses of the world. A craftsman steeped in the traditions of his time, he matured slowly. His dramatic genius came to full fruition in his late forties, with *Orpheus and Euridice* soon to be followed by *Alcestis, Iphigenia in Aulis, Armida* and *Iphigenia on Tauris*.

History has come to recognize Gluck as the most important dramatic composer before Mozart. He has been proclaimed as a revolutionary who cleansed the mid-18th century musical theater of its weaknesses and brought about a sorely needed reform. In fact, Gluck shares this honor with a number of less well-known composers, librettists, choreographers and other creative artists bent on curbing the excesses of crusty formalism and interpretative license which had made the musical theater of their day a mockery of the ideals animating earlier operatic masters: a thorough integration of word and music, a subordination of all contributing elements to fundamental dramatic aims, a striving for dramatic substance of the highest ethical order expressed in the kind of exalted simplicity found in the ancient Greek tragedies.

Luckily, Gluck found a congenial and equally high-minded literary collaborator in the Italian diplomat-poet Ranieri da Calzabigi who wrote the text for several of Gluck's works, including *Orpheus* and *Alceste*. Their collaboration was no less noteworthy than that of later "teams" of Mozart and Da Ponte, Richard Strauss and Hofmannsthal. Unlike Mozart, Gluck was not a universal musician at home in any musical medium. To the core a man of the theater he, like Wagner, saw in the theater the supreme challenge to any composer. To him, to be "theatrical" meant to be truly artistic. This attitude, evident on every page of his music, has kept his masterworks alive through all the metamorphoses of style and public taste.

Orpheus, first performed in Vienna in 1762 in the original Italian was revised extensively for performance in Paris twelve years later. Not only was the vocal line changed to accommodate the French text, but the title-role, originally set for male contralto, was re-written for tenor. In addition, the Paris version contains several numbers not written for the Vienna version. The present edition is the result of a careful amalgamation of the two versions, leaving the title role to a contralto. The Appendix contains two portions of the original Vienna score, now usually omitted in performance.

Orpheus, like its composer, was slow in gaining the recognition it was eventually to achieve. Its very nobility and the stark simplicity of its texture, put it at a disadvantage compared to the lighter fare of comic opera and later the swashbuckling blood-and-thunder works of the romantic period. Yet, among all the works created for the musical stage, none more thoroughly achieves the ideal aim of theater as defined by the ancient Greeks: a *katharsis* or purification of the soul permitted to cleanse itself in the crystal waters of heavenly inspiration.

Walter Ducloux

CAST

ORPHEUS . . . . Contralto
EURIDICE . . . . Soprano
LOVE . . . . Soprano
A BLESSED SPIRIT . . . . Soprano

CHORUS . . . . {
a. Shepherds and Shepherdesses
b. Furies and Monsters
c. Blessed Shadows

The action takes place in Greece, at an unspecified time in antiquity.

SYNOPSIS

ACT I   A Grove Surrounding Euridice's Grave

A group of shepherds and shepherdesses are lamenting the death of Euridice. Orpheus, the celebrated singer and Euridice's bereaved husband, bids the others leave. After pouring out his grief, he appeals to the cruel gods of the Underworld, offering to descend to Hades to abduct his wife from the Realm of the Dead. Amor, the God of Love, informs Orpheus his request has been granted. He shall descend and bring back his wife provided he refrain from looking at her before their re-emergence on earth. Moreover, he is not to tell her of this condition. Orpheus, sensing the torment to which this decree will subject them both, accepts the challenge and proceeds to the Underworld.

ACT II   At the Gates of the Underworld

The terrifying Monsters and Furies guarding the entrance to the Realm of the Dead at first refuse the wanton mortal. Gradually their wrath is soothed by the beauty of Orpheus' singing and he is admitted through the gate. Orpheus proceeds to the Elysian Fields, the domain of the Blessed Spirits.

The Elysian Fields

Orpheus is welcomed by a chorus of Blessed Spirits. Deeply moved by the beauty and peace around him, he soon remembers the purpose of his coming and asks the gods to guide him to Euridice. She is brought in by a group of Blessed Spirits. Orpheus, carefully averting his eyes, leads her on the way back to earth.

ACT III   A Somber Vault in the Underworld

Euridice has become aware of the identity of her rescuer, although she has not seen his face. She is dismayed by his refusal to look at her. Orpheus, unable to give an explanation for his strange behavior, urges her to follow him. Euridice starts doubting his love. When her anxiety turns to despair, Orpheus, no longer able to control himself, turns to her and dooms her forever. She dies. He attempts suicide but is stopped by the God of Love. Orpheus' devotion and loyalty have induced the gods to waive the fatal clause. Amor guides Orpheus and the reawakened Euridice back to earth.

Near the Temple of Love

Happily reunited with their friends and companions, Orpheus and Euridice join in the praise of Love as the dominant force in the world to which everyone should pay a joyous tribute.

CONTENTS

ORPHEUS AND EURIDICE

English translation by
Walter Ducloux

Overture

G. W. von GLUCK

44522cx

Act One

An attractive, secluded grove of laurel and cypress trees surrounding a clearing on which is seen the grave of Euridice. A group of shepherds and shepherdesses are decorating the grave with flowers; others throw incense on the sacrificial flame. Orpheus, slightly downstage from the group, is leaning against a rock and occasionally joins in the lament of the chorus.

La scène représente un bois de lauriers et de cyprès, un séjour agréable mais solitaire qui est entre-coupé pour former une petite plaine contenant le tombeau d'Euridice. — Au lever du rideau et pendant la ritournelle du chœur d'entrée, on voit une troupe de bergers et de nymphes dans la suite d'Orphée et tous portent des couronnes de fleurs et de myrtes; quelques-uns versent de l'encens dans le feu sacré, enguirlandent le marbre et couvrent son tombeau de fleurs, pendant que les autres chantent le chœur suivant qui est interrompu par les plaintes d'Orphée adossé sur le devant contre une pierre et répétant le nom d'Euridice d'une voix gémissante.

SCENE I

Orpheus. Shepherds and Shepherdesses

No. 1 Chorus

No. 2 Recitative

Orpheus *Orphée*

Your sor - row and your grief In - crease my des - o -
Vos plain - tes, vos re - grets aug - men - tent mon sup -

la - tion. In fi - nal, de - vout in - vo - ca - tion Ap -
pli - ce! Aux ma - nes sa - cres d'Eu - ri - di - ce ren -

peal to her gods in your gloom, By strewing flow-ers on her tomb!
dez les su - prê - - mes hon - neurs, et couvrez son tom - beau de fleurs.

No. 3 Pantomime

Lento

No. 4 Chorus

Lento

Soprano: Throughout this grove __ all __ joy has end-ed, Wings of dark-ness

Alto: Ah! dans ce bois lu-gubre et som-bre, Eu-ri-di-ce,

Tenor: Throughout this grove all joy has end-ed, Wings of dark-ness

Bass: Ah! dans ce bois lu-gubre et som-bre, Eu-ri-di-ce,

Lento

sotto voce

have de-scend-ed, Our Eu-ri-di-ce has died. __ Hear our plead-ing,

si ton om-bre, si ton om-bre nous en-tend, sois __ sen-si-ble

have de-scend-ed, Our Eu-ri-di-ce has died. __ Hear our sois sen-

si ton om-bre, si ton om-bre nous en-tend, Hear our plead-ing, sois sen-si-ble a

cresc. *dim.*

No. 5 Recitative

No. 6 Ritornello

(The chorus exits.)-(Les bergers et les nymphes se dispersent dans le bois.)

SCENE II
Orpheus

No. 7 Aria

Long af - ter night must fall,— Hop-ing to hear _ you, hop-ing_to_ hear _ you,
ma voix pen- dant la nuit_ t'appelle en - co - re, t'ap-pelle en - co - re,

hop-ing_to_ hear you.
t'ap-pelle en - co - - - re.

No. 8 Recitative

Orpheus *Orphée*

Dearest shad-ow, my be-lov-ed, My Eu - ri-di-ce, why no re-
Eu-ri- di-ce, Eu-ri-di-ce, om-bre chè - re, ah! dans quels

ply, no hope? Hear your husband, for-lorn, in dis-
lieux es-tu? Ton é-poux gé-mis-sant, in-ter-

may Cry-ing out to the dark-ness for-ev-er, Plead-ing in
dit, é-per-du, te de-man- de sans ces-se, à la na-

44522

20

44522

No. 10 Recitative

hap-pi-ness and beau-ty.
u - ne main trem-blan-te.
Eu - ri - di-ce has died, Death I myself pre-
Eu - ri - di - ce n'est plus, et *je respire en-*

fer. Gods, give her back to me — Or let me die with her!
cor. Dieux, ren-dez-lui la vi-e, ou don-nez-moi la mort!

No. 11 Aria

Andantino
Orpheus *Orphée*

Filled with_ woe_ and de - spair, Rend-ing_ with_ sighs_ the_
*Plein de_ trouble et d'ef - froi, que de_ maux loin_ de_*

air,_ My heart is_ sink - ing, My heart_ is_ sink -
toi,_ mon cœur en - du - re, mon cœur_ en - du -

ing.   The brook a - lone_ shall know_ How
re;   té - moins de_ mes mal - heurs, sen -

No. 12 Recitative

24

wife. / vir!

Without fear I descend To your re-gions in-fernal Where the
Je sau-rai pé-nétrer jusqu'au sombre ri-vage, mes ac-

pleas of my grief Will at last cool your ire. In your breast this hatred e-ter-nal Shall sub-
cents douloureux fléchi-ront vos rigueurs; je me sens as-sez de cou ra-ge pour bra-

SCENE III

The God of Love. Orpheus

Amor *L'Amour*

side before my pas-sion's fire! Your plea is not in vain. Your ap-
ver tou-tes vos fu-reurs. L'a-mour vient au se-cours de l'a-

peal has been heed-ed. The God of Love, I come here To grant you your quest. For to your
mant le plus ten-dre. Ras-su-re-toi, les dieux sont tou-chés de ton sort. Dans les en-

wish the gods have acceded: You shall find your belov-ed Where in death she must rest.
fers tu peux te rendre; va trou-ver Eu-ri-di-ce au sé-jour de la mort.

No. 13 Aria

L Amor *L'Amour*

Let your ten-der lyre's ____ sweet en-deav - or, Fill with its
Si les doux ac-cords ____ de ta ly - re, si tes ac-

har - mo-ny the air. Its song ____ the sav-age fiends Shall be-calm in their
cents ____ mé-lo-di-eux ap-pai - - sent la fu-reur des ty-rans de ces

lair. ____ Yours she will be __ once __ more,
lieux, ____ tu __ la ra-mè - ne - ras

Yours to be-hold for-
du té - nébreux em -

ev - er. Yours she will be __ once __ more,
pi - re, tu __ la ra-mè - ne - ras

Yours to be-hold for - ev - - er.
du té-nébreux em - pi - - re.

44522

attacca

No. 14 Recitative

No. 15 Aria

Amor
L'Amour

Lento e grazioso

This is the gods' command And obey it you must To be wor-thy — of their trust.
Tels sont de Ju-pi-ter les su-prêmes décrets. Rends-toi di-gne de ses bien-faits!

In
Sou-

si - lence to suf - fer, Your loved one so near, — Is part of this of - fer.
mis au si - len - ce, con-trains ton dé - sir, — fais - toi vi - o - len -

fer. But soon will be end - ed Your tor - ment and fear. — Yes, soon will be
ce, bien - tôt à ce prix tes tour - ments vont fi - nir, — bien - tôt à ce

Meno lento

end - ed your tor - ment and fear. To love in dis - tress — Shows
prix tes tour-ments vont fi - nir. Tu sais qu'un a - mant di-

p

p

44522

30

44522

Meno lento

soon will be end-ed Your tor-ment and fear.___ Yes. soon will be
tôt à ce prix tes tour-ments vont fi - nir,___ bien - tôt à ce

(The God of Love disappears.) (L'Amour s'éloigne.)

end-ed Your tor-ment and fear.
prix tes tour-ments vont fi - nir.

SCENE IV
Orpheus

Moderato

No. 16 Recitative

Orpheus *Orphée*

How won-drous! Did I dream? Eu-ri-di-ce will re-turn,
Qu'en - tends-je? *qu'a-t-il dit?* *Eu-ri-di-ce vi-vra!*

be mine for-ev - er? A god of light, a god of mer-cy Will bring her
mon Eu-ri-di - ce! *Un dieu clé-ment,* *un dieu pro-pi-ce me la ren-*

back? But I must turn a - way From the one I love so
dra! *Mais quoi!* *je ne pour-rai,* *re - ve - nant à la*

44522

faith be de-fend-ed! If Love should fail me now, My own life shall be end-ed!
maux que j'en-du-re. Dou - ter de ton bien-fait se - rait te faire in-ju-re.

Mighty gods, I pro-ceed, O-beying your command!
C'en est fait, dieuxpuissants, j'ac-cep-te vo-tre loi.

(See Appendix page 141)
(Voir Supplément page 141)

No. 17 Aria

Allegro maestoso

M

Orpheus *Orphée*

O' Love, I call you to
A - mour, viens rendre à mon

guide me,   Firm - ly to stand   be - side me.   Your
â - me   ta   plus   ar - den - - te _ flam - me;   pour

won - drous ar - mor _ hide me   In   dan - - ger and _ in
cel - le _ qui m'en - flam - me,   je   vais   bra - ver _ le tré -

fear!   O   Love, I _ call _ you to guide _ me,   Firm - ly to stand be -
pas.   A - mour, viens rendre a mon a - - me   ta _ plus ar - den - te _

side _ me.   Your won - drous ar - mor   hide _____
flam - me;   pour cel - le qui m'en - flam - - - - - -

me, Yes, it will hide ___ me ___ In ___ dan - ger and in fear! Now
-me, ___ je vais bra - ver, ___ bra - - ver ___ le tré - pas. L'en -

death shall hold her no long-er, shall hold her no long-er.
fer envain nous sé - pa - re, en vain nous sé - pa - re,

My heart will prove the stronger, And Love ___ will guide her
les monstres du tar - ta - re ne m'é - pou - van - tent

here, Yes, Love will walk be - side ___
pas. Je sens croî - tre ma flam - - -

36

me In ev 'ry dan - ger, ev - 'ry fear! Now death shall hold her no
- me; je vais bra - ver___ le tre - pas. L'en - fer en vain nous sé-

cresc.

f

long - er, shall hold her no long - er.
pa - re, en vain nous sé - pa - re,

f

My heart will prove the strong - er, And
les mon - stres du tar - ta - re ne

Love will guide her here. Firm - ly walk - ing be-
m'é - pou - van - tent pas. Je sens croî - tre ma

rinf

p

side flam -

me – The God – of
– me, – je vais bra-

Love will guide her here,
– ver le tré - pas,

The God of Love will guide her here.
je vais bra - ver le tré - pas.

End of Act I
Fin du premier acte

Act Two

A frightening, rocky landscape near the gates of the Underworld, veiled in a dark mist occasionally pierced by flames. The dance of the Furies and Monsters is interrupted by sounds of the lyre of the approaching ORPHEUS. When he comes into view they all join in the ensuing chorus.

Une contrée épouvantable, hérisée de rochers, au delà du Styx; au loin s'élève une fumée épaisse, sombre, les flammes y jaillissent de temps en temps. Les spectres et les esprits commencent une danse qu'Orphée interrompt par l'harmonie de sa lyre; à la vue d'Orphée toute la troupe entonne le premier chœur qui suit.

SCENE I

Orpheus. Furies and monsters of the underworld.

No. 18 Dance of the Furies

No. 19 Harp Solo Chorus

(*Second orchestra backstage.*)
2ᵈ orchestre derrière le théâtre.

No. 20 Dance of the Furies

attacca

No. 21 Chorus

(Thé Furies dance around Orpheus to frighten him.)
(Pendant le chœur les esprits dansent autour d'Orphée pour l'effrayer.)

C

When howl - ing hell - hound's roar, Foam-drip - ping fangs a - jar,

à l'af - freux hur - - le-ment du Cer - bère é - - cu-mant

When howl - ing hell - hound's roar, Foam-drip - ping fangs a - jar,

à l'af - freux hur - - le-ment du Cer - bère é - - cu-mant

Bar him the door.

et ru - gis - sant!

Bar him the door.

et ru - gis - sant!

D

Ter-ror shall strike his heart, Tear-ing his mind a-part, When howl - ing

Que la peur, la terreur s'em - pa - rent de son cœur à l'af-freux

Ter-ror shall strike his heart, Tear-ing his mind a-part, When howl - ing

Que la peur, la terreur s'em - pa - rent de son cœur à l'af-freux

No. 22 Solo with Chorus

No. 23 Chorus

(The chorus answers Orpheus in a somewhat milder manner, showing signs of compassion)
(Le chœur apaisé répond à Orphée avec un peu plus de pitié dans l'expression.)

Soprano: Hav-ing de-fied your fear Tell us who brought you here! Here is for
Alto: Qui t'a-mène en ces lieux, mor-tel pré-somp-tu-eux? C'est le sé-
Tenor: Hav-ing de-fied your fear Tell us who brought you here! Here is for
Bass: Qui t'a-mène en ces lieux, mor-tel pré-somp-tu-eux? C'est le sé-

life no room, Noth-ing but night and gloom, None but the cries of The damned in their
jour af-freux des re-mords dé-vo-rants et des gé-mis-se-ments et des tour-
life no room, Noth-ing but night and gloom, None but the cries of The damned in their
jour af-freux des re-mords dé-vo-rants et des gé-mis-se-ments et des tour-

doom.— Hav-ing de-fied your fear Tell us who brought you here!
ments. Qui t'a-mène en ces lieux, mor-tel pré-somp-tu-eux?
doom.— Hav-ing de-fied your fear Tell us who brought you here!
ments. Qui t'a-mène en ces lieux, mor-tel pré-somp-tu-eux?

No. 24 Aria

No. 25 Chorus

(*In a milder manner*)   (*Encore plus apaisé.*)

No. 26 Aria

Un poco lento · Orpheus *Orphée*

No. 27 Chorus
(*Almost completely subdued*) (*Encore plus doux.*)

44522

No. 28 Dance of the Furies

After the dance has started Orpheus enters the underworld. Towards the end of the dance, the Furies and monsters gradually disappear.

Après le commencement de cette danse, Orphée entre dans les enfers; vers la fin de la danse les spectres et les esprits disparaissent peu à peu.

The Elysian Fields, domain of the Blessed Spirits. An enchanting landscape with
bushes, flowers, brooklets, etc.

Une contrée enchanteresse des champs Elysées pleine de superbes buissons, de fleurs, de ruisseaux etc.

SCENE II

Chorus of the Blessed Spirits. Euridice.

Chœur des esprits bienheureux à l'Elysée; ensuite **Euridice.**

(The scene opens with a dance of the Blessed Spirits.)
(Le chœur ouvre la scène par une danse.)

No. 29 Ballet

No. 30 Ballet

No. 31 Ballet

Dolce, con espressione

Da Capo al Fine.

No. 32 Aria with Chorus

68

44522

(*During the postlude Euridice and the Blessed Spirits slowly withdraw. Orpheus is lost in admiration.*)
Pendant le postlude disparaissent Euridice et les esprits bienheureux. Orphée est perdu dans l'admiration.

SCENE III
Orpheus

No. 33 Aria

Orpheus *Orphée*

Out of the   sky,   won - drous and
Quel nouveau ciel   *pa - - re ces*

bright,   To charm   my
lieux!   *Un jour   plus*

eye   down   came a   light.   A - -
doux   s'offre   à mes   yeux.   *Quels*

you, on-ly you, My be-lov-ed my wife, Eu-ri-di-ce, can give me back my
toi, doux ob-jet de ma flam-me, toi seule y peux cal-mer le trou-ble de mon

O

life!
â-me.

Once a-
Tes ac-

gain to lis-ten to her voice,
cents ten-dres et tou-chants,

P

In her smile to re-joice,
tes re-gards sé-dui-sants,

Once more to see her ...
ton doux sou-ri-re

44522

Grant me, you gods, _____ this on - ly fa - vor!
sont les seuls biens _____ que je dé - si - re.

cresc.

SCENE IV

Orpheus and Chorus of the Blessed Spirits

(Orpheus looks around as the Chorus approaches him.)
(Orphée regarde autour de lui, le chœur s'en approche.)

No. 34 Chorus

Andantino

Soprano: Come, the Bless - ed Fields in -
Alto: *Viens dans ce sé - jour pai-*
Tenor: Come, the Bless - ed Fields in -
Bass: *Viens dans ce sé - jour pai-*

Andantino

dolce, sotto voce

vite _____ you, Hus - band ten - der, love shall de - light you, Come, and
si - ble, e - poux ten - dre, a - mant sen - si - ble, viens ban-
vite _____ you, Hus - band ten - der, love shall de - light you, Come, and
si - ble, é - poux ten - dre, a - mant sen - si - ble, viens ban -

76

44522

ri-di-ce,

She will greet you.
va pa - raî-tre,

ri - di - ce will meet you,

di - ce va pa - raî-tre,

Yes, Eu - ri - di - ce will

Eu - ri - di - ce va pa -

Yes, Eu - ri - di - ce, will

Eu - ri - di - ce va pa -

greet ___ you,

raî - - tre

greet ___ you,

raî - - tre

Nev - er to de - part a -

a - vec de nou - veaux at -

Nev - er to de - part a -

a - vec de nou - veaux at -

gain.

traits,

gain,

traits,

Yes, Eu - ri - di - ce will nev - er leave you a - gain.
va re - naître a - vec de nou - veaux at - traits.

a - vec de nou - veaux at - traits.

Nev - er to de - part ___ a - gain.

a - vec de nou - veaux at - traits.

No. 35 Ballet

No. 36 Recitative and Chorus

SCENE V
Euridice, Orpheus and Chorus of the Blessed Spirits

No. 37 Chorus

(The Chorus leads Euridice to Orpheus. Without looking at her or being recognized by her, he takes
Euridice est ramenée à Orphée par le chœur; sans la regarder, il saisit sa main et

her hand and leads her away. The curtain falls slowly.)
l'emmène. — Le rideau se baisse lentement.

End of Act II
Fin du deuxième acte.

Act Three

A dark subterranean vault indicating a labyrinth of passageways amidst overhanging rocks covered with moss.
Une caverne sombre avec un labyrinthe plein de couloirs obscurs et entourée de rochers mousseux, tombants.

SCENE I
Orpheus, Euridice

(*Orpheus still leads Euridice by the hand, without looking at her.*)
(*Orphée mème encore Euridice par la main sans la regarder.*)

No. 38 Recitative

84

44522

44522

Orpheus (*noticing that she is near him, he takes her hand to lead her away*)
Orphée (*sent qu'elle est pres de lui, il saisit sa main voulant l'emmener.*)

stow on his wife   A sin-gle lov-ing glance!   Oh do not yield, dear one, To fear and
ports in-no-cents   de sa fi-dèle é-pou-se.   Par tes soupçons ces-se de m'ou-tra-

Euridice (*indignantly withdrawing her hand*)
(*indignée retire sa main*).

doubt!   Why re-turn me to life   If now you cast me out?   Gods,   your compas-sion is
ger.   Tu me rends à la vie,   et c'est pour m'af-fli-ger!   Dieux,   re-pre-nez un bien-

vain and un-want-ed.   Lone — ly and be-trayed,   leave me here!
fait   que j'ab-hor — re!   ah!__ cru-el é-poux,   lais-se-moi!

No. 39 Duet

Andante   Orpheus *Orphée*

Come!
Viens!

See how your sor-rows ag-grieve me,   See how your sor-rows ag-
Suis un é-poux qui t'a-do-re,   suis un é-poux qui t'a-

E

Might - y gods, I now im-
Dieux,   soy-ez-moi fa - vo -

Si - lent I still must re - main.
non, je ne par-le-rai pas,

Si - lent I still must re - main.
non, je ne par-le-rai pas.

plore you   Oh   see   me weeping here be - fore   you!
ra - bles,   voy - ez   mes pleurs,dieux se - cu - ra - bles!

Might - y gods, I now im-plore   you,   Oh   see   me weeping here be -
Dieux,   soy-ez-moi fa - vo - ra - bles,   voy - ez   mes pleurs,dieux se - cou-

legato

My dis - tress   is past en - dur - ing, My dis - tress   is
Quels tour - ments in-sup-por - ta - bles,quels tour-ments   in -

fore   you!   My dis - tress   is past en - dur - ing,   My dis - tress is
ra - bles!   Quels tour - ments in-sup-por - ta - bles,   quels tourments in -

Più lento

past en - dur - ing.   Oh,   what de - spair   Has   my   tor - tured heart to
sup - por - ta - bles!   quel - les ri - gueurs   mê - lez - vous à vos fa -

past en - dur - ing.   Oh, ___ what de - spair   Has   my   tor - tured heart to
sup - por - ta - bles!   quel - les ri - gueurs   mê - lez - vous à vos fa -

cresc.

90

Tempo 1

bear, Has my tor-tured heart to bear!
veurs, mê-lez-vous à vos fa-veurs!

bear, Has my tor-tured heart to bear!
veurs, mê-lez-vous à vos fa-veurs!

F

Tell me your se-cret, I be-seech you! Oh,
Par-le, ré-ponds, je t'en sup-pli-e, ré

tell me, I be-seech you!
ponds, je t'en sup-pli-e.

My se-cret I can-not teach you, And
Dût-il m'en cou-ter la vi-e, non,

Tell me!
Par-le!

si-lent must re-main, And si-lent must re-
je ne par-le-rai pas, non, je ne par-le-rai

44522

Più lento

Weep-ing be - fore you, My dis - tress is past en - dur - ing. What mis-
voy - ez mes pleurs! Quels tour - ments in - sup - por - ta - bles, quels tour-

fore you, My dis - tress is past en - dur - ing. What mis-
pleurs! Quels tour - ments in - sup - por - ta - bles, quels tour-

for - tune past en - dur - ing Has my tor - tured heart to bear!
ments in - sup-por - ta - bles mê - lez - vous à vos fa - veurs!

for - tune past en - dur - ing Has my tor - tured heart to bear! What de -
ments in - sup-por - ta - bles mê - lez vous à vos fa - veurs! Quel-les ri-

What de - spair Has my tor - tured heart to bear! Oh, what despair Has my
Quel-les ri - gueurs mê - lez - vous à vos fa - veurs, quel-les rigueurs mê-lez-

spair Has my tor - tured heart to bear! Oh, what despair Has my
gueurs mê - lez - vous à vos fa - veurs, quel-les rigueurs mê-lez-

tor - tured heart to bear! *(They separate. Each one, on a different side of the stage, leans against a rock or a tree.)*
vous à vos fa - veurs! *(Chacun d'eux se dirige vers un autre côté de la scène où ils restent adossés à un arbre ou à un rocher.)*

tor - tured heart to bear!
vous à vos fa - veurs!

44522

No. 40 Recitative

Allegro Euridice

Yet, why should he per - sist In this om - i - nous si - lence?
Mais d'où vient qu'il per-siste à gar-der le si-len-ce?

Moderato

What is the se - cret seal - ing his lips?
Quels se - crets veut-il me ca-cher?

Could it be that he tore me From heav - en - ly bliss A - new to kill me by dis-dain and cold-ness?
Au sé - jour du re - pos de-vait - il m'ar - ra - cher pour m'ac - ca - bler de son in-dif - fé - ren-ce?

Ah, what griev - ous de-spair! My blood is slow - ly freez - ing And death's be-numb-ing breath A -
Oh de - stin ri - gou - reux! Ma for - ce m'a - ban-don - ne, le voi - le de la mort re -

Allegro moderato

round me fills the air.
tom - be sur mes yeux!

I am cold,
Je fré - mis,

and I shake
je lan - guis,

as with fe - ver,
je fris - son - ne,

Am faint - ing,
je trem - ble,

feel - ing weak. . .
je pâ - lis,

My throb - bing heart beat - ing wild - ly in fear and
mon cœur pal - pi - te, un trou - ble se - cret m'a -

ter - ror,
gi - te,

All my sens - es are gripped with
tous mes sens sont sai - sis d'hor -

fright! Close in once more, e - ter - nal night!
reur, et je suc - combe à ma dou - leur.

pp

cresc.

f

No. 41 Aria and Duet

96

-ture me so, why tor - - - - ture me so?
les tour-ments, que pour_____ les tour-ments?

Duet — Duo
Andante

In — re - cent en - chant-ment, Sur - - round - ed by
Orpheus *Orphée* *Je goû - tais   les   char - mes d'un re - pos sans a -*

Andante

Her sus-pi - cion and doubt
Ses in - ju - stes soup - çons

poco f

beau - ty,   by   heav - - - en - ly beau-ty,   Now
lar - mes, d'un re - pos_____ sans_ a - lar-mes,   le

Sink dag-gers in my — heart.   Her
re - dou - blent mes tour - ments!   Que

bit - ter,   re - ject - ed,   Be - reaved — and — de -
trou - ble,   les lar - mes   rem - plis - sent au - jour -

sor - row   and sad - ness
di - re?   que fai - re?

44522

woe.___ Oh fiend-ish de-lu——sion, Oh Treach-er-ous il-lu——
ments? For - tune en-ne - mi—— e, quel - le bar - ba - ri——

sion, You give me back a life Full of tor-ment and woe. Why, gods a-bove, oh
e! ne me rends-tu la vi - e que pour les tour - ments, ne me rends-tu la

why Do you tor——ture me so, why tor——ture me
vi - e que pour _____ les tour - ments, que pour _____ les tour-

so?
ments?

No. 42 Recitative

No. 43 Aria

Tempo I **P**

fright.   Now my love has gone for - ev - er.   All my days have turned to
cœur!   *J'ai per - du mon Eu - ri - di - ce, rien n'é - ga - le mon mal-*

night.   From my heart, gone for - ev - er Ev - 'ry ray of hope and
heur; sort cru - el! quel - le ri - gueur, rien n'é - ga - le mon mal-

light, hope and light Have died for - ev - er None can know my bit - ter
heur! sort cru - el! quel - le ri - gueur! je suc - combe à ma dou-

plight, my bit - ter plight, my bit - ter plight.
leur, à ma dou - leur, à ma dou - leur!

No. 44 Recitative

Orpheus *Orphée*

My o-verwhelming grief Shall find its grim con-clusion. I nev-er can sur-
Ah! puis-se ma dou-leur fi-nir a-vec ma vi-e! Je ne sur-vi-vrai

vive A fate too harsh to bear. So once a-gain I shall de-scend to
point à ce der-nier re-vers. Je touche en-cor aux por-tes des en-

Ha-des And soon shall be with her, Eu-ri-di-ce, my wife.___
fers, j'au-rai bien-tôt re-joint mon é-pou-se ché-ri-e.

Adagio

Yes, I shall fol-low you, my love, To the
Oui, je te suis,___ tendre ob-jet de ma

grave, stay with you for-ev-er, for-ev-er.
foi, je te suis, at-tends-moi, at-tends-moi!

No one shall ev-er take you from me Af-ter death does u-
Tu ne me se-ras plus ra-vi-e, et la mort pour ja-

44522

SCENE II
The God of Love. Orpheus and Euridice.

(Orpheus tries to stab himself with a dagger.)
(Lorsqu'il est sur le point de se tuer, Amour apparaît.)

Amor (wrests the dagger from Orpheus)
L'Amour (lui arrache le poignard).

Orpheus *Orphée*

nite What can-not live a-part! De - sist, O mor - tal! Great gods, who can mock my Despair,
mais va m'u - nir a - vec toi. Ar - rête, Or - phé - e! O ciel! Qui pour-rait en ce jour

Amor *L'Amour*

can intrude on my grief, On my sa - cred re - solve? — Mas-ter your despair and your
re - te - nir le trans-port de mon âme é - ga - ré - e? Cal - me ta fu - reur in - sen-

rav-ing! See here! I am the God of Love Who rules the des-ti - ny you chal-lenge.
sé - e; ar - rête, et re - con-nais l'a-mour qui veil - le sur ta des-ti - né - e.

Orpheus *Orphée*   **Amor** *L'Amour*

What brings you here to me? You have withstood the test Of de - vo - tion and love, And your
Qu'e-xi-gez-vous de moi? Tu viens de me prou-ver ta con - stance et ta foi; je vais

suff-'ring and pain shall be end - ed. Eu - ri - di-ce,
fai - re ces-ser ton mar-ty - re. Eu - ri - di - ce!

a - wak - en! He who loves you so true Shall have his just re -
re - spi - re! Du plus fi - dèle é - poux viens cou-ron-ner les

Orpheus *Orphée*   Euridice   Orpheus *Orphée*

ward! My Eu-ri-di-ce! My Or-pheus! Al-might-y gods, Our grat-i-tude shall be un-
feux. Mon Eu-ri-di-ce! Or-phé-e! Ah! ju-stes dieux! quelle est no-tre re-con-nais-

Amor *L'Amour*

bounded. Your fears and doubts you find unfounded. But now without de-lay To brighter spheres a-
san-ce! Ne dou-tez plus de ma puis-san-ce! Je viens vous re-ti-rer de cet af-freux sé-

bove, To en-joy, as you may, The de-lights of your love!
jour, jou-is-sez dé-sor-mais des plai-sirs de l'a-mour!

SCENE III

The magnificent Temple of Love. The God of Love, Orpheus and Euridice enter preceded by a large group of shepherds and shepherdesses. The return of Euridice is celebrated by joyous songs and dances.
Un magnifique temple consacré à l'amour.—L'Amour, Orphée, Euridice. Devant eux marche une nombreuse troupe de bergers et de bergères fêtant le retour d'Euridice par leur chant et leurs joyeuses danses.

No. 45 Chorus and Soloists

Allegro leggiero

deav - or, Rule for - ev - er _ beaut-y's do - main! His chains will un -

spi - re sert l'em - pi - re _ de la beau - té; sa chaine a - gré -

deav - or, Rule for - ev - er beaut-y's do - main! His chains will un -

spi - re sert l'em - pi - re de la beau - té; sa chaine a - gré -

ite _ us, Charm, and de - light _ us. Slaves, we are hap-py in his

a - ble est pré - fé - ra - ble, est pré - fé - ra - ble à la

ite us, Charm, and de - light us.

a - ble est pré - fé - ra - ble,

bless - ed _ reign. Slaves, we are hap-py in his bless - ed _ reign.

li - ber - té, est pré - fé - ra - ble à la li - ber - té.

Slaves, we are hap-py in his bless - ed reign.

est pré - fé - ra - ble à la li - ber - té.

C Amor *L'Amour*

Pained, in an-guish, in doubt and sor-row,— Man-y a heart knows
Dans les pei-nes, dans les a-lar-mes— je fais sou-vent lan-

rain— and— storm. Yet, the sun will— shine to-mor-row,—
guir les— cœurs; mais dans un in-stant mes char-mes—

Lov-ing and heal-ing, so ten-der and warm, Lov-ing and heal-ing, so
font pour ja-mais_ou-bli-er— mes ri-gueurs, font pour ja-mais_ou-bli-

ten-der and warm.
er_ mes ri-gueurs.

D

Let love tri-
L'a-mour tri-

Let love tri-
L'a-mour tri-

44522

E Euridice

Jeal-ous and wild, my — heart may suf-fer, Ten-der thoughts may flee my — breast;
Si la cru - el - le — ja - lou - si - e   a   trou - blé mes — ten - dres dé - sirs,

Yet true — love will — have to — of - fer   Heal - ing   balm — and —
les   dou - ceurs dont elle   est sui - vi - e,   sont des   chai - nes —

sweet - est — rest,   Heal - ing — balm — and —   sweet - est — rest.
de — plai - si - rs,   sont des — chai - nes —   de — plai - sirs.

f **F**

Let love   tri - um - phant! Be guide in all en -
L'a - mour   tri - om - phe et   tout ce qui re -

Let love   tri - um - phant Be guide in all en -
L'a - mour   tri - om - phe et   tout ce qui re -

116

44522

No. 46 Ballet

No. 47 Gavotte

Allegro

Fine.

Dal Segno al Fine.

No. 48 Ballet

Vivace

H

No. 49 Minuet

No. 50 Trio

No. 51 Ballet

No. 52 Ballet

W

No. 53 Chaconne

44522

End of Opera
Fin de l'opéra.

Appendix
No. 1 Postlude to Recitative No. 16
If Aria No. 17 (allegedly by Bertoni) is to be cut.

(See page 33, Measure 6)

Supplément.
I. Postlude au récitatif N⁰ 16,
si l'air N⁰ 17 (attribué à Bertoni)
doit être supprimé.
(Voir page 33 mesure 6.)

(Thunder and lightning. Orpheus leaves quickly.)
(Eclair et tonnerre, Orphée s'enfuit.)

End of Act I
Fin du premier acte.

II. Ballet

Allegro

Fine.

Dal Segno al Fine. %

G. SCHIRMER'S
CLOTH BOUND VOCAL SCORES OF
STANDARD OPERAS

BEETHOVEN.	Fidelio *(German and English)*
BELLINI.	La Sonnambula *(Italian and English)*
BELLINI.	Norma *(Italian)*
BIZET.	Carmen *(French and English)*
CHARPENTIER.	Louise *(French and English)*
DONIZETTI.	L'Elisir d'Amore *(Italian and English)*
DONIZETTI.	Lucia di Lammermoor *(Italian and English)*
FLOTOW.	Martha *(German and English)*
GLUCK.	Orpheus and Euridice *(French and English)*
GOUNOD.	Faust *(French and English)*
GOUNOD.	Roméo et Juliette *(French and English)*
HERBERT.	Natoma *(English)*
HUMPERDINCK.	Hansel and Gretel *(English)*
LEONCAVALLO.	Pagliacci *(Italian and English)*
MASCAGNI.	Cavalleria Rusticana *(Italian and English)*
MASSENET.	Manon *(French and English)*
MOZART.	Cosí fan Tutte *(Italian and English)*
MOZART.	Don Giovanni *(Italian and English)*
MOZART.	Le Nozze di Figaro *(Italian and English)*
MOZART.	Die Zauberflöte *(German and English)*
NICOLAI.	The Merry Wives of Windsor *(English)*
OFFENBACH.	Les Contes d'Hoffmann *(French and English)*
PONCHIELLI.	La Gioconda *(Italian)*
PUCCINI.	La Bohème *(Italian and English)*
PUCCINI.	Madama Butterfly *(Italian and English)*
PUCCINI.	Tosca *(Italian and English)*
ROSSINI.	Il Barbiere di Siviglia *(Italian and English)*
SAINT-SAENS.	Samson et Dalila *(French and English)*
SMETANA.	The Bartered Bride *(English)*
TCHAIKOVSKY.	Eugene Onégin *(English)*
TCHAIKOVSKY.	The Queen of Spades (Pique-Dame) *(English)*
THOMAS.	Mignon *(French and English)*
VERDI.	Aida *(Italian and English)*
VERDI.	Un Ballo in Maschera *(Italian and English)*
VERDI.	Otello *(Italian and English)*
VERDI.	Rigoletto *(Italian and English)*
VERDI.	La Traviata *(Italian and English)*
VERDI.	Il Trovatore *(Italian and English)*
WAGNER.	Der Fliegende Holländer *(German and English)*
WAGNER.	Götterdämmerung *(German and English)*
WAGNER.	Lohengrin *(German and English)*
WAGNER.	Die Meistersinger von Nürnberg *(German and English)*
WAGNER.	Parsifal *(German and English)*
WAGNER.	Das Rheingold *(German and English)*
WAGNER.	Siegfried *(German and English)*
WAGNER.	Tannhäuser *(German and English)*
WAGNER.	Tristan und Isolde *(German and English)*
WAGNER.	Die Walküre *(German and English)*
WEBER.	Der Freischütz *(German and English)*